Unicorns

PAINTINGS BY SUSAN SEDDON BOULET
♦ COLORING BOOK ♦

Now I will believe that there are unicorns.
—William Shakespeare, *The Tempest*

The enchanting unicorn has long been a favorite subject of authors and artists of fairy tale and fantasy. Often described as strong, fleet of foot, and fierce in battle, this legendary beast was seen as a symbol of grace and purity, and could be tamed by a pretty young maiden. Since the Middle Ages, the unicorn has commonly been pictured as a white steed with a spiraled horn on its forehead. The magnificent unicorn lives on in dreams and myths, and, perhaps most vividly, in the artwork of visionary artist Susan Seddon Boulet (American, b. Brazil, 1941–1997). The twenty-one paintings shown on the insides of this coloring book's covers are playful and imaginative yet powerful, as the artist calls attention to the relationship between unicorns and humans. You can use these vibrant images to guide you as you fill in the drawings, or to help inspire your own versions. We've left two pages at the back of the book blank so that you can dream up unicorns or other mythical animals of your own.

Pomegranate

Line drawings adapted from paintings by Susan Seddon Boulet (American, b. Brazil, 1941–1997).

Pomegranate Communications, Inc.
19018 NE Portal Way, Portland OR 97230
800 227 1428   www.pomegranate.com

Color reproductions © 2015 E. Boulet
Line drawings © Pomegranate Communications, Inc.

Item No. CB173

Designed by Carey Hall. Line drawings by Cory Mimms.

Printed in Korea

25 24 23 22 21 20 19 18 17 16   10 9 8 7 6 5 4 3 2 1

Distributed by Pomegranate Europe Ltd.
Unit 1, Heathcote Business Centre, Hurlbutt Road
Warwick, Warwickshire CV34 6TD, UK
[+44] 0 1926 430111
sales@pomeurope.co.uk

1.

3.

4.

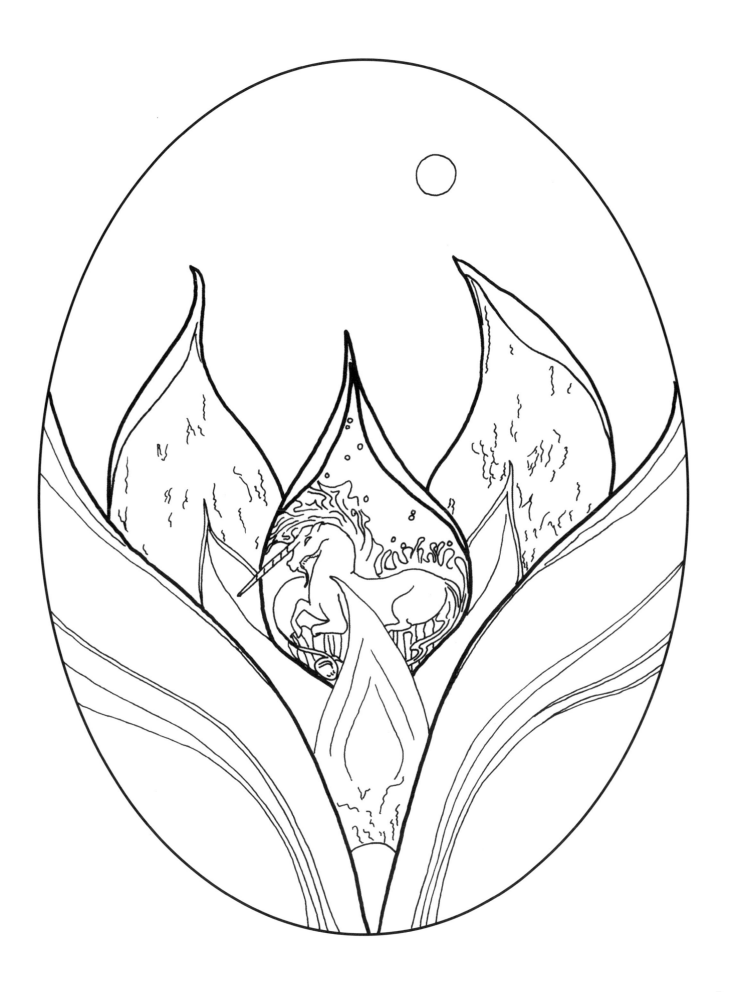

6.

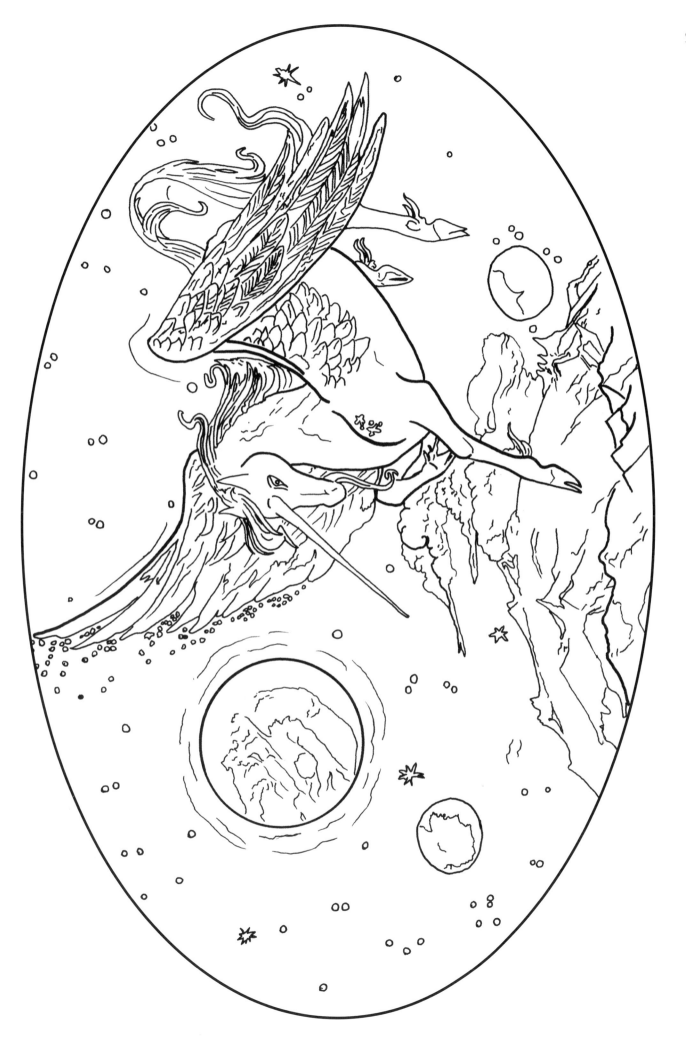

Draw and color your own picture here!

Draw and color your own picture here!